How To Overcome Bullying

Anthony Juliano

Another Quality Book Published By:
LEGACY BOOK PUBLISHING
1850 Lee Rd., STE. 223 Winter Park, FL 32789
www.LEGACYBOOKPUBLISHING.com

This is the story of a kid named AJ, and how he overcame bullying.

AJ was bullied in elementary school.

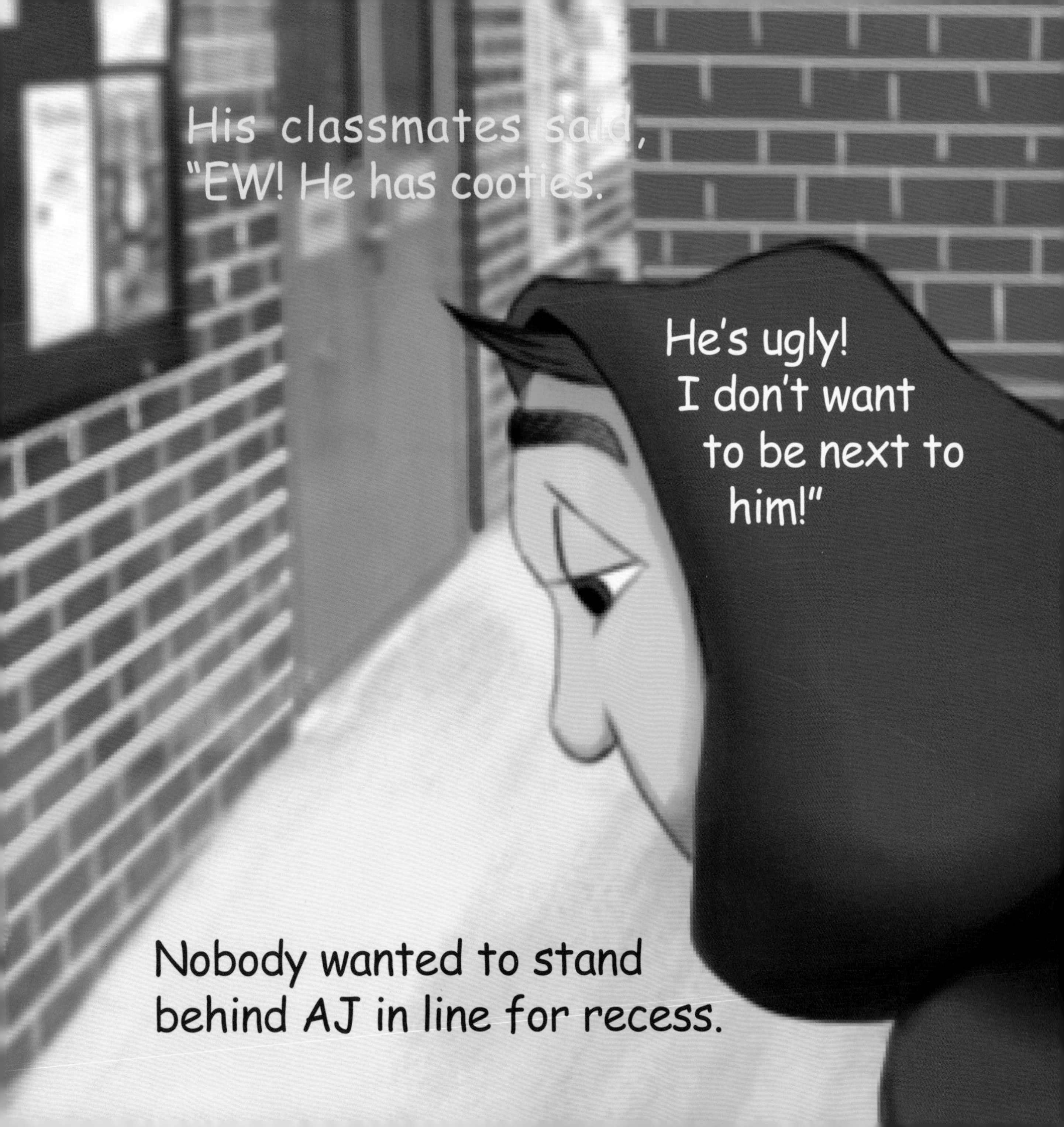

His classmates said,
"EW! He has cooties.
He's ugly!
I don't want
to be next to
him!"

Nobody wanted to stand
behind AJ in line for recess.

AJ's teacher, Ms. Gable, made the whole class sit inside during recess to write AJ apology letters.

AJ got to play outside for recess by himself.

It was fun, but he wished he had a friend to play with.

AJ went to a new school in 5th grade.

He was excited for a fresh start.

He met two really tall guys named Shawn and Peter.

Shawn and Peter loved to play a game called *Chase the Man with the Ball*. Shawn and Peter chased AJ, even when he didn't want to run.

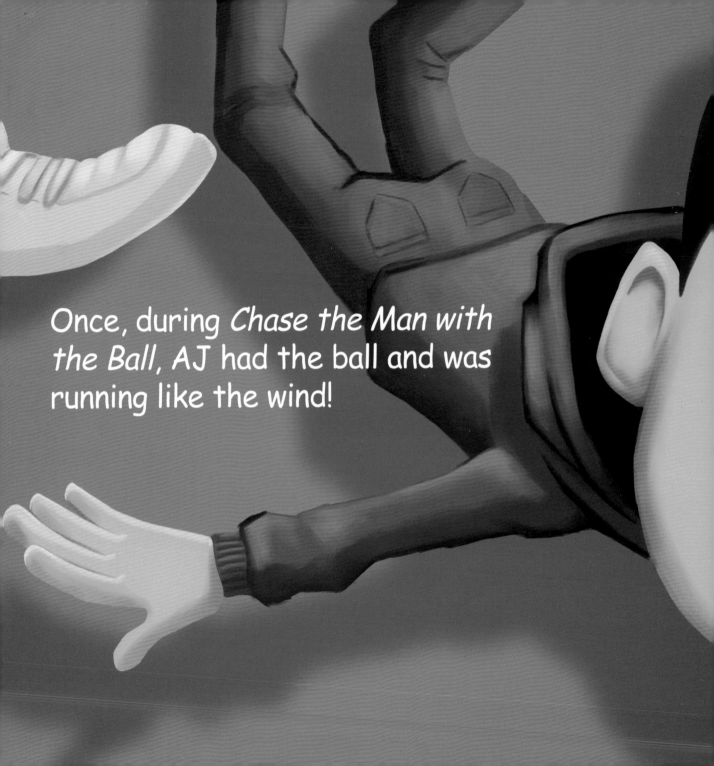

Once, during *Chase the Man with the Ball*, AJ had the ball and was running like the wind!

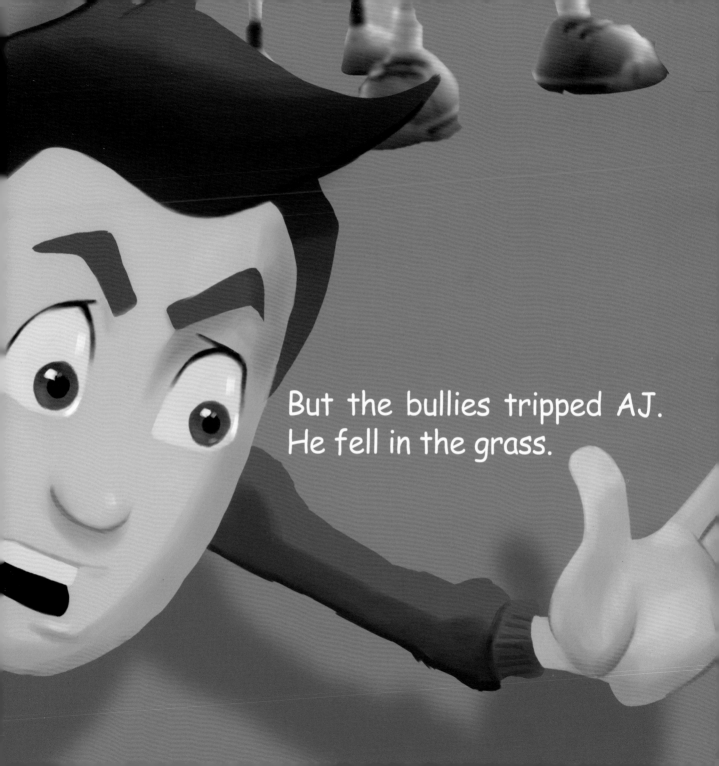

But the bullies tripped AJ.
He fell in the grass.

The bullies took AJ's ball and hit him in the face with it.

AJ was hurt and sad. He just wanted to make friends at his new school.

While he was down, Shawn and Peter made fun of AJ's shorts. "HA HA, your shorts are so short they show your knees!"

"Stop bullying me!" AJ said.

"What are you gonna do about it?"

AJ had tried standing up for himself, but the bullies would not listen.

He needed help, so he told the principal that Shawn and Peter were bullying him.

The principal brought them into his office. They all talked.

It turned out that AJ, Shawn, and Peter had lots in common; they liked the same sports and games. The bullies apologized. AJ forgave them and they became friends.

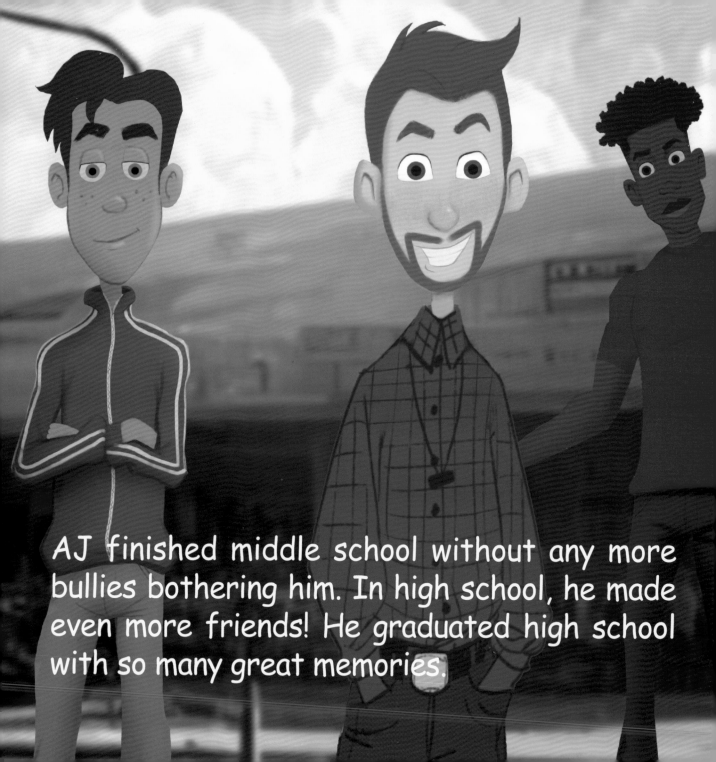

AJ finished middle school without any more bullies bothering him. In high school, he made even more friends! He graduated high school with so many great memories.

REPUBLIX

AJ now works for one of the biggest retail stores in the world! He has lots of friends at work, but more importantly, he believes in himself.

This book is dedicated to every person in this world who has been bullied.

You each have a unique personality and you are worth knowing; never believe a bully if they tell you otherwise. Accept yourself and you will succeed and go places in life. If you treat others well, you have already defeated bullies just by being a good example.

On this journey, AJ learned that every person has their own unique personality and strengths. He learned that friendships grow when we try to understand each other, and that the world can be a very happy place to live.

If you are being bullied, don't give up hope.

Here are some resources to help you:

Stopbullying.gov

Cfchildren.org/resources/
bullying-prevention-
resources/

If you need to talk to somebody, call 988.
988lifeline.org